THE VALUE OF
CURIOSITY
13
The Tale of Christopher Columbus

The New ValueTales® Series Created by
Spencer Johnson, M.D.
#1 New York Times, USA Today Bestselling Author

THE VALUE OF
DEDICATION
14
The Tale of Albert Schweitzer

The New ValueTales® Series Created by
Spencer Johnson, M.D.
#1 New York Times, USA Today Bestselling Author

The Tale of Eleanor Roosevelt

The New ValueTales® Series Created by
Spencer Johnson, M.D.
#1 New York Times, USA Today Bestselling Author

THE VALUE OF
RESPONSIBILITY
16
The Tale of Ralph Bunche

The New ValueTales® Series Created by
Spencer Johnson, M.D.
#1 New York Times, USA Today Bestselling Author

THE VALUE OF
SAVING
17
The Tale of Benjamin Franklin

The New ValueTales® Series Created by
Spencer Johnson, M.D.
#1 New York Times, USA Today Bestselling Author

THE VALUE OF
KINDNESS
18
The Tale of Elizabeth Fry

The New ValueTales® Series Created by
Spencer Johnson, M.D.
#1 New York Times, USA Today Bestselling Author

THE VALUE OF
CREATIVITY
19
The Tale of Thomas Edison

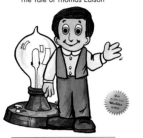

The New ValueTales® Series Created by
Spencer Johnson, M.D.
#1 New York Times, USA Today Bestselling Author

THE VALUE OF
TRUTH & TRUST
20
The Tale of Cochise

The New ValueTales® Series Created by
Spencer Johnson, M.D.
#1 New York Times, USA Today Bestselling Author

THE VALUE OF
IMAGINATION
21
The Tale of Charles Dickens

The New ValueTales® Series Created by
Spencer Johnson, M.D.
#1 New York Times, USA Today Bestselling Author

THE VALUE OF
FORESIGHT
22
The Tale of Thomas Jefferson

The New ValueTales® Series Created by
Spencer Johnson, M.D.
#1 New York Times, USA Today Bestselling Author

THE VALUE OF
DETERMINATION
23
The Tale of Helen Keller

The New ValueTales® Series Created by
Spencer Johnson, M.D.
#1 New York Times, USA Today Bestselling Author

THE VALUE OF
GIVING
24
The Tale of Ludwig Van Beethoven

The New ValueTales® Series Created by
Spencer Johnson, M.D.
#1 New York Times, USA Today Bestselling Author

GIFT

This Book Is A Gift

For: _____

From: _____

THE VALUE OF
SHARING

The Tale of the Mayo Brothers

ValueTales®
Timeless Values
In Entertaining Tales

For more information about The New ValueTales®:
1-800-515-0848

www.ValueTales.com

THE VALUE OF SHARING

The Tale of the Mayo Brothers

The New ValueTales® Series Created and Edited By
Spencer Johnson, M.D.

Based on
Original Text by
Spencer Johnson, M.D.
and
Original Illustrations by
Steve Pileggi

Candle
PUBLISHING

Candle
PUBLISHING
Better to light a candle
Than curse the darkness

The New ValueTale® Books Are Available At:
http://www.ValueTales.com
1 – 800 – 515 – 0848

Published in the United States of America by Candle Publishing.

Volume 5, Edition 1, *The New ValueTales® Series*

Published in 2007 under title: The Value of Sharing: The Tale of the Mayo Brothers.
First ed. published in 1977 under title: The ValueTale of the Mayo Brothers: The Value of Sharing.

Library of Congress Control Number: 2007930383

ISBN 978-1-934288-04-7

Personal Values; Historical Figures; Role Models; Juvenile Literature; Doctors; Surgery; Medicine; Sharing.

Manufactured in the United States of America.

WELCOME

This fictional tale is about The Mayo Brothers — Will and Charlie — real people who lived in Minnesota in the 19th and 20th centuries.

This imaginative story is based on many historical events that really happened and it shows how useful the value of sharing can be. More historical facts are found on page 64.

Now let's have fun with our story — *The Value of Sharing: The Tale of The Mayo Brothers...*

ONCE upon a time...

a long time ago, in a land called Minnesota, there lived two brothers — Will Mayo and Charlie Mayo.

Will and Charlie lived in the little town of Rochester, where their father was a country doctor. They loved to ride out across the prairies with him when he made his calls.

They were proud and happy whenever their father helped a sick person feel well again.

But Dr. Mayo couldn't always help. Once when the boys came home after they had been out with their father, they felt very sad.

"What's the matter?" their mother asked.

"Last week Dad operated on a boy to try to save his life," said Charlie. "Well, Dad couldn't save him."

"He got an infection," Will added, "and Dad couldn't stop the infection."

The doctor came in and sat down. He looked very tired. "It's so hard to stop infections," he sighed. "If only I knew how to keep them from starting."

"Just a minute," said Mrs. Mayo. "I have to get something. I'll be right back." And she went out smiling.

Why do you suppose she was smiling at a time like this?

She was smiling because she had just thought of a way to help her husband. Dr. Mayo had asked his wife to look at all the medical journals he received and to let him know about what might be important to him.

She came back in a few minutes with a journal. "Look at this!" she said to her husband. The doctor began to read.

"Wonderful!" he exclaimed. "A man named Louis Pasteur has proved that germs cause infections. And you can see germs through a microscope."

He put down the journal. "Oh, if only I could go to New York," he said. "I could study Pasteur's methods there! But we don't have a lot of money for the trip."

Mrs. Mayo suggested, "If it is important, we could use the money we have saved."

Dr. and Mrs. Mayo agreed that it was *very* important, and so the Mayo family set out on a journey of more than a thousand miles.

In New York, Dr. Mayo, and other doctors, used a microscope to see germs that cause infections. He learned that germs can't live in very clean places, and boiling things in hot water could kill germs. Most important, he learned how to stop infections during an operation.

Dr. Mayo shared what he learned with his wife and the boys. He said, "To use what I have learned, I will need my own microscope. But they are expensive."

Mrs. Mayo suggested, "Maybe we could borrow money on our house, and you could buy the equipment you need to help the people of Minnesota."

That is exactly what they decided to do. And before long, the Mayo family returned to their home in Minnesota.

Will and Charlie danced with excitement when their father carried the microscope into the house. They could hardly wait for him to put it down, so they could look through it.

"Why does it have such a funny name?" asked Charlie.

"Because 'micro' means 'very small'", said their father. "'Scope' means 'to look at'".

"I see," said Will. "So we can use it to look at very small things — like germs — right?"

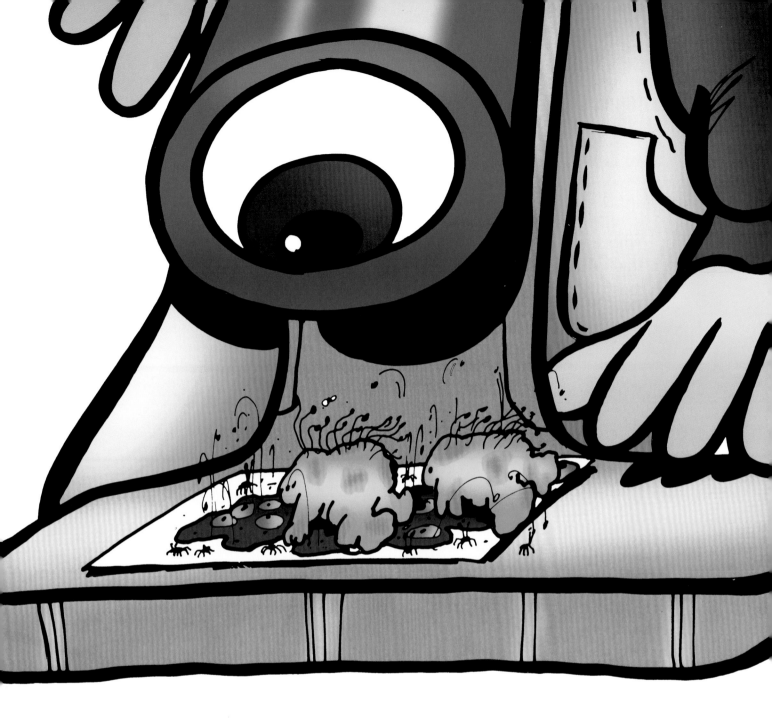

"Exactly," said Dr. Mayo. "But look carefully. That's a very expensive piece of equipment."

The boys were careful, and they learned to properly use a microscope before most children learn their multiplication tables.

There was also something else they did while they were still very young — a thing that surprised many people.

What do you think it was?

Young Will and Charlie not only watched their father operate, they often *helped* him with the operation.

In those days, there was no hospital in southern Minnesota, so Dr. Mayo often performed operations in people's homes.

The boys were so small that they had to stand on wooden boxes to see what their father was doing. And even though they were young, their dad talked to them as if they were grown up.

He shared his knowledge with them. He explained exactly what was going on and how the boys could help.

Will and Charlie were usually good at helping. But sometimes they did not pay attention. They daydreamed about other things.

One day, during an operation, the boys used their imaginations.

They looked over at their father's scissors, and imagined that the shiny scissors had two twinkling eyes.

"I must be seeing things!" thought Will.

"That pair of scissors is looking at me," Charlie said to himself.

And then something even stranger happened! The scissors seemed to talk to them.

"Hi, boys!" the scissors seemed to say. "My name is Two-Sides and I'd like to be your friend."

The boys were smart so they knew that scissors cannot talk. It was just a fun way to listen to their own thoughts. They asked, "How come you're called Two-Sides? That's a funny name."

"Not for me," said the scissors. "Have you ever seen scissors that could cut with only one blade on one side? Of course not. You need two sides to work together." Then he added, "That's called sharing."

"Your dad is sharing right now. He's explaining this operation to you. So he's doing his part, isn't he? What about you? Are you doing your part? Are you listening?"

The boys were silent for a moment. They knew they had not been listening to their father.

"There are two sides to sharing," Two-Sides said. "Sharing is giving and receiving."

"It's like talking...," Will began.

"And listening, " Charlie added.

But before Two-Sides could say anything, Will and Charlie heard a very real voice. "Boys!" their father said. "Please. Pay attention!"

Will and Charlie jumped. They saw that their father had been waiting for Will to hand him what he needed. Charlie hurried to take the instruments out of boiling water and put them on the table near Will.

"Sorry, Dad," said Will. "I'm afraid we were daydreaming." And he handed Dr. Mayo the surgical scissors he wanted.

After that, the boys remembered what Two-Sides had said. They listened very carefully to what their father was teaching them.

But Will and Charlie weren't always so attentive at school. In fact, they were only average students.

Their teachers probably never imagined that they would grow up to become two of the most famous doctors in the world.

Will and Charlie imagined that they took Two-Sides everywhere with them. "We think you're nice," said Charlie. "And we like the things you say about sharing. How would you like to go to the circus with us?"

"Great," he said. "I can't think of anything I'd like to share more than a circus." And so the three went off to look at the elephants and tigers and all the other circus animals.

When Will, Charlie and Two-Sides reached the big circus tent, little Charlie saw something that puzzled him.

Can you guess what it might be?

The boys noticed that many, many, clowns scrambled out of one tiny house. "I don't understand," said Charlie. "Where are they all coming from?"

Before Will or Two-Sides could answer, the boys heard their mother calling to them from outside the circus tent. "Will!" cried Mrs. Mayo. "Charlie! Come quickly! Your father wants you!"

The boys forgot about the circus as they raced off to meet their father at the home of the town blacksmith.

"Can you help my wife, Doctor?" the man was saying as the boys arrived. "Her stomach is very big and she's in a lot of pain and can hardly breathe. I'm afraid she going to die!"

Dr. Mayo put his arm around the man. "There now," he said kindly. "You and I can work together to help save her."

"Me?" said the blacksmith. "Work with you? But I'm not a doctor. What can I do?"

"I'm going to need special instruments for your wife's operation," said the doctor. "You're a blacksmith. You can take a piece of metal and heat it in the fire. Then you can pound it into any shape you like.

"Your wife has a tumor growing deep inside her, and the instruments I have aren't long enough to reach it. You can make the instruments I need to reach the tumor."

Of course the blacksmith set to work right away, with the boys and Two-Sides watching.

While the blacksmith hammered at the metal, Dr. Mayo talked with the sick woman. "We're going to help you," he promised. "My boys are here now, and my wife will come with other doctors who will assist with the operation. You'll be all right. You'll see."

When Mrs. Mayo and the other doctors arrived at the blacksmith's house, everything was as clean as it could be before the operation began.

"You see," said Two-Sides, "your father is using what he's learned. He's doing everything he can to keep an infection from starting."

Will said, "Wouldn't it be terrible if the doctors in New York hadn't shared that with him?"

When the operation was over, Dr. Mayo told the blacksmith, "Your wife is going to be just fine."

When they saw the blacksmith's happy smile, the boys looked at each other and knew what they both were thinking.

"We want to be doctors, too," Will and Charlie told their mother. "We want to help people like father does."

"Of course you can be doctors," Mrs. Mayo said. "But to be really good doctors you need to understand how people think and feel, not just how their bodies work."

Dr. Mayo said, "It's helpful to read good books like those by Charles Dickens so you can learn how people feel."

As Will, the older brother, grew up, he learned that it took more than reading to become a doctor. He had to work and save money so that he could afford to go to medical school.

Will got a job working in a drugstore after school. He swept and dusted. He also learned how to make all kinds of medicine. And he saved his money.

Years later, when he was almost ready to leave for medical school, he didn't go straight home after work. He surprised his mother and father and Charlie by asking them to meet him at the general store.

Two-Sides was curious. "What is happening?" he asked.

"Today, I'm going to buy Charlie a new suit," said Will. And he did!

"I can't believe it!" Charlie said as he stared at himself in the mirror. "A new suit! Brand new! I've never had a new suit!" He gave his brother a big hug.

"I figured you must be pretty tired of always wearing my old clothes," said Will. He was smiling proudly.

Two-Sides whispered, "It feels good, doesn't it, when you share with someone?"

Later, Will imagined that he took Two-Sides with him to medical school. He followed Two-Sides' advice, too. When his teachers were talking, he listened and learned. And of course, he always shared what he learned with his brother Charlie when he went home.

After many years of hard work, Will graduated from medical school. He was happy to be able to help his father care for sick people. Because his father was already called Dr. Mayo, everyone in town began to call him Dr. Will.

"Gee, Will," said Charlie, "now I can drive around with you, just the way we used to go around with Dad."

Charlie was very proud of his brother Dr. Will.

One hot summer day, Charlie and Dr. Will had been out seeing patients in the country. They stopped the carriage when they noticed the sky was growing dark. The wind had stopped completely, and everything was strangely quiet.

"What is it?" whispered Charlie. He sounded scared.

"Look!" Will pointed. Charlie saw a funnel-shaped cloud off in the distance — a tornado!

"Giddy-up!" cried Will, and he whipped the horse into action. "We'll be safer in town!"

But Will was wrong. As they raced over a wooden bridge and onto the main street of town, the tornado roared down after them.

Charlie and Will reached the far side of the bridge just an instant
before the vicious wind hurled the bridge up into the air.

Timbers shattered into bits and pieces as they smashed to the ground
near the two brothers.

The brothers were blown out of their carriage when the wind screamed past them. They were swept down the main street of Rochester like two big leaves blown from a tree.

The tornado raced through the town. It smashed buildings and tossed the wreckage into the air.

Then, as suddenly as it had come, the storm sped away across the countryside.

Charlie and Will looked around, amazed. Somehow they had not been hurt. But there were lots of injured people all around them.

Dr. Will and Charlie set to work helping people who were hurt. Dr. Mayo came running and the town hall was turned into an emergency hospital. Temporary beds were set up. A group of nuns acted as nurses, and everyone else in the town pitched in and helped.

But the town hall wasn't very clean. Some of the wounded people got infections. Some even died.

"We need a hospital," said one of the nuns after the tragedy was all over. "We need a clean place where we can take care of people who are sick or hurt."

"Indeed we do," Dr. Mayo agreed.

"We'll raise the money and build the hospital," said the nuns, "if you and your sons will be the doctors."

"What a great idea!" cried Dr. Will. "Charlie is going to medical school soon. When he finishes, there'll be three Mayo doctors to share the work that has to be done."

Two-Sides grinned. "That's another good thing about sharing," he said. "It makes the work easier."

It took a long time to build the hospital.

But, then, it took a long time for Charlie to become a doctor. While he studied, Dr. Will and Dr. Mayo took care of people.

Sometimes their patients paid them with a chicken from the hen house. Sometimes they paid with a basket of apples from the orchard. Sometimes they couldn't pay at all.

"Don't worry," Dr. Will always said. "We only want to help you get better."

When Charlie came home from medical school, he found that many patients were coming to his father and his brother for help.

And he laughed the first time one of the patients called him "Dr. Charlie."

"That sounds pretty good," he said to Two-Sides.

After the hospital was opened, the three Mayo doctors were able to help even more people.

Dr. Will and Dr. Charlie had learned the newest and best methods of scientifically treating patients, and shared what they knew with each other.

Their father, however, also knew how important it was for a good doctor to be aware of patients' feelings, too.

"Never forget that we're taking care of people," he would say, "and there's more to pay attention to than just their sickness."

Soon people were coming to the Mayos from all over Minnesota.

"The Mayo doctors are good at their work," said these patients. "Their surgical rooms are clean. They use carbolic acid to kill the germs. Almost no one ever dies because of infection at the hospital in Rochester."

Before long, patients weren't the only people who came to see the Mayos.

Can you guess who else came?

Doctors and nurses from nearby towns came. They wanted to see just how the Mayos were able to help so many people.

Two-Sides said to Will and Charlie, "You used to stand on boxes to watch your dad operate. Now other doctors are standing on boxes to watch you!"

"If they can learn from us, we're glad," said Dr. Will.

"We're always happy to share what we know," declared Dr. Charlie.

However, both Mayo Brothers realized that there were things they didn't know — things they needed to find out.

"Why don't you and I take turns traveling?" said Will to Charlie one day. "One of us can stay at home and look after our patients while the other visits the best hospitals and the best doctors in the world. Then the one who's been traveling can come home and share what he's learned. That way we can keep learning and be better doctors."

"What a great idea!" Dr. Charlie exclaimed. And from that time on the Mayos traveled all over the world, learning more and more about medicine.

You could see one of the Mayo Brothers at almost any major meeting of doctors. They were easy to recognize because they did not wear fancy clothes or grow important-looking beards like the others. But in spite of their simple ways, the Mayos *did* impress the other doctors.

Everyone listened carefully whenever Charlie or Will spoke at a meeting. Why? Because the two young men from Minnesota had proved that they could do many types of operations very well.

More people got better in the little town of Rochester, Minnesota, than in just about any other place in the world.

Both Dr. Will and Dr. Charlie often said, "My brother and I."

Charlie told the other doctors. "My brother and I would be glad to share what we know and you're welcome to come to our clinic whenever you want and see what we do."

Charlie always talked in a slow, friendly way and had a good sense of humor. He sounded a lot like his famous friend Will Rogers.

He said, to Two-Sides' delight, "One of the nice things about sharing knowledge is that after you give it to someone else, you still have it!"

Doctors from all over the world accepted Charlie's invitation.

There were no wooden boxes in the operating rooms now.

Visiting doctors could sit and look up into mirrors over the operating tables, to see exactly what was going on.

The seats they sat on could slide from one side to another, so that the visitors could move to see what was going on when Will and Charlie moved during an operation.

The fame of the Mayo brothers spread.

Surgeons came from Europe and South America to spend weeks watching Will and Charlie, and to learn what they knew.

Later, when their father was seventy years old, Dr. Mayo left most of the work at the hospital to Dr. Will and Dr. Charlie. Dr. Mayo knew that his patients were well looked after, and now he had time to do something else that he had always enjoyed doing.

What do you suppose he did?

Dr. Mayo loved to travel. In fact, he and his wife went around the world twice by the time he was eighty-seven years old!

Most of the time Dr. and Mrs. Mayo traveled just for fun. But sometimes, when he was in far-off lands, the old doctor visited other doctors and saw their hospitals.

And whenever he saw something new that might help people, he told Will and Charlie about it as soon as he got home.

Back in Rochester, things were getting pretty crowded at the little building the Mayos used for a clinic.

"Look at all those people," Dr. Will said one day when the waiting rooms were especially full. "There seem to be more people every day."

"We really need a bigger clinic," said Dr. Charlie.

"I want to talk to you about that," said Dr. Will. "Come on into my office. You can come too, Two-Sides."

When they were in his office, Dr. Will said, "We have a lot of money, even though we've never charged people who could not afford to pay us. It's because we've helped so many other people who could pay."

Dr. Charlie said, "It's certainly more than we need to live on."

Dr. Will agreed. "So why don't we find a way to share the money with people who are sick?"

"We could build a new building," said Dr. Charlie. "Then we could help more people. And we could help support young doctors who want to stay here and study with us."

"Great!" shouted Two-Sides. "You've grown into men who really know the value of sharing."

The two men smiled and said, "Thank you so much for your wonderful help! We shall always remember what you helped us discover."

Later, the Mayo brothers did build a larger clinic. Then, for twenty more years they kept saving.

One dollar out of every two they made was saved and invested to share later with people who were ill.

When they felt they had enough, the brothers went to see the head of the University of Minnesota.

"My brother and I now have two million dollars," Dr. Will told the university president. "We'd like to give it to the university to help students and young doctors who want to study medicine at our clinic."

"What a wonderful gift," said the surprised man. "But why are you doing this?"

"Sometimes people don't understand," said Dr. Charlie. "But it is really very simple. It makes us feel good when we share what we have with others."

Can you imagine how proud Two-Sides felt?

Two-Sides whispered, "You both are sharing so well. It's time for me to go now and help other children learn about sharing."

Dr. Will and Dr. Charlie said, "Thank you, Two-Sides, for helping us to see all the wonderful things that sharing with others can achieve."

As their friend disappeared, they looked around them. They saw that so many other doctors had come to the Mayo Clinic. Some returned to their own hometowns, having learned a lot, while others stayed on to help out at the clinic.

"It's great!" said Dr. Charlie. "More and more doctors are helping more and more people."

All through this busy, happy time, one person was most proud of the brothers. She had watched the two little Mayo boys, since they were babies, grow up into two fine men. Can you guess who she was?

It was their mother!

Mrs. Mayo was over eighty, and she still read the medical journals, just as she had read them for her husband. But now she looked for articles by Dr. William Mayo or Dr. Charles Mayo. And often she found them, for her sons shared their knowledge by writing more than a thousand articles for the medical journals.

While they had never been interested in fame, the Mayo brothers had become famous because of their valuable work. They were often honored. Even the President of the United States was proud to talk with the Mayos.

But Dr. Will and Dr. Charlie were quiet, humble men. "I feel uncomfortable when people treat me as if I were special," Dr. Will always said. And Dr. Charlie declared that the biggest reason they succeeded was that they picked the right parents.

But the boys remembered what Two-Sides always said. When you have the value of sharing, you can balance both receiving and giving.

So the Mayo brothers received the praise and the honors, and were thankful for it.

However, no matter how many honors they warmly received, the Mayo brothers' greatest joy came from something else. It came from seeing some of the very best doctors in the world come to the little town of Rochester, Minnesota.

Today, people still come from all over the world to be helped by doctors at the Mayo Clinic.

The Mayos shared what they had and they enjoyed it. They always felt happy when they saw the good that came from it.

As our story nears its end, what do *you* think?

What you may want to do in your own life may be very different from the Mayo Brothers.

You can choose whatever you want for yourself.

Whatever you choose, you may find that when you share, in big and small ways, you can be happier too. Just like our friends the Mayo Brothers.

Then perhaps, you can have fun making the world a little better place — by sharing what you have learned with others!

The End

DISCUSSION

Now that you know about *The Value of Sharing: The Tale of the Mayo Brothers* —

What do *you* think?

 What did you like most about the story?

 Who did Will and Charlie Mayo share things with?

 What do you think would have happened if the Mayo Brothers did not share with others?

 How do you feel when *you* share?

 How could you use *The Value of Sharing,* in big and little ways, to be happier in your own life?

HISTORICAL FACTS
THE MAYO BROTHERS
William 1861-1939
Charlie 1865-1939

The Mayo Brothers were able to share a great many things with each other during their lifetimes. They were the only two boys of five children born to Louise Abigail Wright and William Worrall Mayo. While the boys enjoyed their sisters, Gertrude, Phoebe, and Sarah, the brothers were drawn to each other in a very special way.

The boys' father was born in England and came to America in 1845 at the age of 26. After graduating from the University of Missouri Medical School in 1854, marrying, and having three daughters, he settled in the pioneer village of Le Sueur, Minnesota. There he became the proud father of his first son, Will. As a doctor for the Army, near the end of the Civil War, Dr. Mayo, Sr. moved his family in 1863 to the site of the district recruiting station in Rochester, Minnesota, where his second son, Charlie was born. It was here that he was to share his medical knowledge with his sons, and they with the world.

Will and Charlie grew up at the same time that surgery itself was growing up. Charlie Mayo was born in 1865, the same year that Sir Joseph Lister first announced the success of his "carbolic spray" method for controlling surgical infections. Louis Pasteur was still trying to convince most of the medical world that germs were actually the cause of infection.

A year after Charlie's birth, the clinical thermometer first came into use and three years later, the first (wooden) stethoscope was introduced.

Dr. Mayo, Sr., then nearly 52 years old, was determined that he and his boys would grow with the medical times. In 1871, he left his remote Minnesota village to update his knowledge and skills at New York's Bellevue Hospital. He became one of the first doctors in the country to use a microscope in his practice.

It seemed natural that both boys would become doctors. Will graduated from the University of Michigan Medical School in 1883 and Charlie from Chicago Medical School in 1888. One year later, St. Mary's Hospital opened with forty beds and three Mayo physicians — a 70 year-old father and his two sons. And, as we know, their nearby medical offices became the beginning of a cornerstone in medicine — The Mayo Clinic.

The Mayo brothers were scientists and humanitarians. They published over 1,000 scientific papers in the medical journals about their work. What they didn't tell many people, however, was what they did behind the scenes for the less fortunate people they cared for. As many as 30 percent of their patients were surprised and relieved to find the handwritten words PAID IN FULL on the Mayos' bills — bills which they could not otherwise afford. And regardless of how much money the patients had, no one was ever charged more than 10 percent of his or her annual income, no matter how expensive the treatment. And every dollar they collected on bills over $1,000.00 went to help other sick people.

They were very close during their more than seventy years of life. And they were almost inseparable in death. After Dr. Charlie died unexpectedly of pneumonia on May 26, 1939, Dr. Will died quietly on July 28, 1939 — only two months after Charlie.

As successful as they had been as surgeons, it has been said that their real success was probably as brothers. Whenever one of them was singled out for an honor by a medical society, a university, or a government, they would each begin to accept any honor with the same four words, "My brother and I..."

ENJOY THE ENTIRE VALUETALES® SERIES!

1	2	3	4	5	6	7	8	9	10	11	12	13	14	15	16	17	18	19	20	21	22	23	24
BELIEVING IN YOURSELF	HONESTY	FAIRNESS	COURAGE	SHARING	HUMOR	LEARNING	HELPING	UNDERSTANDING	PATIENCE	RESPECT	FRIENDSHIP	CURIOSITY	DEDICATION	CARING	RESPONSIBILITY	SAVING	KINDNESS	CREATIVITY	TRUTH AND TRUST	IMAGINATION	FORESIGHT	DETERMINATION	GIVING
PASTEUR	CONFUCIUS	BLY	ROBINSON	MAYO BROTHERS	ROGERS	CURIE	TUBMAN	MEAD	WRIGHT BROTHERS	LINCOLN	ADDAMS	COLUMBUS	SCHWEITZER	ROOSEVELT	BUNCHE	FRANKLIN	FRY	EDISON	COCHISE	DICKENS	JEFFERSON	KELLER	BEETHOVEN

VALUETALES® SUBSCRIPTION
TIMELESS VALUES DELIVERED MONTHLY!

You can provide children with a new ValueTales® book each month with your
ValueTales® subscription. $16^{95}/month + s&h

Phone 1-800-515-0848
Visit www.ValueTales.com

THE VALUE OF
BELIEVING IN YOURSELF
The Tale of Louis Pasteur

1

The New ValueTales® Series Created by
Spencer Johnson, M.D.
#1 New York Times, USA Today Bestselling Author

THE VALUE OF
HONESTY
The Tale of Confucius

2

The New ValueTales® Series Created by
Spencer Johnson, M.D.
#1 New York Times, USA Today Bestselling Author

THE VALUE OF
FAIRNESS
The Tale of Nellie Bly

3

The New ValueTales® Series Created by
Spencer Johnson, M.D.
#1 New York Times, USA Today Bestselling Author

THE VALUE OF
COURAGE
The Tale of Jackie Robinson

4

The New ValueTales® Series Created by
Spencer Johnson, M.D.
#1 New York Times, USA Today Bestselling Author

THE VALUE OF
SHARING
The Tale of the Mayo Brothers

5

The New ValueTales® Series Created by
Spencer Johnson, M.D.
#1 New York Times, USA Today Bestselling Author

THE VALUE OF
HUMOR
The Tale of Will Rogers

6

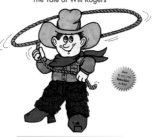

The New ValueTales® Series Created by
Spencer Johnson, M.D.
#1 New York Times, USA Today Bestselling Author

THE VALUE OF
LEARNING
The Tale of Marie Curie

7

The New ValueTales® Series Created by
Spencer Johnson, M.D.
#1 New York Times, USA Today Bestselling Author

THE VALUE OF
HELPING
The Tale of Harriet Tubman

8

The New ValueTales® Series Created by
Spencer Johnson, M.D.
#1 New York Times, USA Today Bestselling Author

THE VALUE OF
UNDERSTANDING
The Tale of Margaret Mead

9

The New ValueTales® Series Created by
Spencer Johnson, M.D.
#1 New York Times, USA Today Bestselling Author

THE VALUE OF
PATIENCE
The Tale of the Wright Brothers

10

The New ValueTales® Series Created by
Spencer Johnson, M.D.
#1 New York Times, USA Today Bestselling Author

THE VALUE OF
RESPECT
The Tale of Abraham Lincoln

11

The New ValueTales® Series Created by
Spencer Johnson, M.D.
#1 New York Times, USA Today Bestselling Author

THE VALUE OF
FRIENDSHIP
The Tale of Jane Addams

12

The New ValueTales® Series Created by
Spencer Johnson, M.D.
#1 New York Times, USA Today Bestselling Author